A Word to Paren

*Your testimonies are my delight;
they are my counselors.—Psalm 119:24*

What a tremendous blessing it is when a child delights in God's Word. The truth then becomes an ever-present counselor or advisor to the child whether the child is at home interacting with siblings, on the playground at school, or alone with his thoughts. The Word of God is powerful and active. It can inform the thinking of a child, change his heart, and direct his will.

Surely it is the calling of every Christian parent to thoroughly acquaint his or her child with God's glorious Word. You hold in your hands one tool for helping you to keep the Word present in your child's life. Each coloring picture has been thoughtfully and creatively drawn to help illustrate the truth of a verse of the Bible. These verses have been specifically chosen to help your child fight the fight of faith. They are part of a Bible memory program called Fighter Verses.

How to Use the Coloring Book

- Read the Bible verse with your child. Explain any unfamiliar words or concepts.

- Talk about how the picture illustrates the truth of the verse.

- Discuss the summary, helping your child to very practically apply the truth to his life. What is God asking of him? What should he think, be, and do in response to God's Word?

- Instruct your child to think about the verse as he or she colors the picture. If you are using the Coloring Book as part of the *The Fighter Verses Study*, have your younger child(ren) color the picture while the family is discussing the devotional questions. Encourage the younger child(ren) to participate in the discussion as he is able.

- Encourage and help your child to memorize the verse or part of it. Use stickers to mark off the

"Verses I Have Memorized" chart in the as your child hides God's Word in his heart.

- Review the verses periodically so that the verses are retained in long-term memory.

- Pray with your child using the words or thoughts of the verse or summary.

- Talk about the verse and the truth of it when you "sit in your house, and when you walk by the way, and when you lie down, and when you rise" (Deuteronomy 6:7). Let God's Word be the "constant hum" in the background of your life as well as in your conscious, deliberate focus. Make it the ever present delight and counselor to your family.

- Encourage your child to share the verse with someone else.

May the Lord bless your efforts to encourage your child to actively engage with the Word of God.

**Let the word of Christ dwell in you richly, teaching and admonishing
one another in all wisdom, singing psalms and hymns and spiritual songs,
with thankfulness in your hearts to God.—*Colossians 3:16***

Table of Contents

1. Deuteronomy 7:9 5
2. Deuteronomy 10:12-13 6
3. John 1:12-13 7
4. Romans 11:33-36 8
5. Romans 12:1-12 9
6. Psalm 56:3-4 10
7. Psalm 62:5-7 [8] 11
8. Romans 8:1 12
9. 1 John 2:15-17 13
10. Philippians 2:5-7 14
11. Philippians 2:8-9 15
12. Philippians 2:10-11 16
13. Philippians 2:12-13 17
14. James 1:2-3 18
15. James 1:4-5 19
16. Psalm 1:1-2 20
17. Psalm 1:3-4 21
18. Psalm 1:5-6 22
19. Colossians 3:1-3 23
20. Ephesians 4:26 24
21. Isaiah 40:28-29 25
22. Isaiah 40:30-31 26
23. Psalm 86:5-7 27
24. 1 Timothy 2:5 28
25. 1 Peter 1:3-5 29
26. Ephesians 6:10-11 30
27. Ephesians 6:12-13 31
28. Ephesians 6:14-15 32
29. Ephesians 6:16-17 [18] 33
30. Philippians 1:6 34
31. Matthew 10:28 35
32. Romans 1:16 [17] 36
33. Matthew 11:28-30 37
34. Psalm 20:6-7 [8] 38
35. James 1:12 39
36. 2 Corinthians 9:6-7 40
37. 2 Corinthians 9:8 41
38. 2 Corinthians 12:9 [10] 42
39. Isaiah 64:4 43
40. Titus 3:4-6 44
41. Isaiah 46:9-10 [11] 45
42. Proverbs 1:10 46
43. Proverbs 3:5-6 [7] 47
44. Proverbs 19:11 48
45. John 15:5 49
46. John 14:2-3 50
47. Psalm 125:1-2 51
48. Psalm 141:3-4 52
49. 1 John 1:8-9 53
50. Psalm 23:1-2 54
51. Psalm 23:3-4 55
52. Psalm 23:5-6 56
Bible Memory Tips 57
About Fighter Verses 58
Verses I Have Memorized 59

Note about Fighter Verses that include a number in [brackets]

A few of the Fighter Verse passages (e.g., Psalm 62:5-7 [8]) include a verse number set apart with [brackets]. Verses in brackets are optional additional memory verses. Only the un-bracketed verses are actually included in the Fighter Verses Scripture memory program.

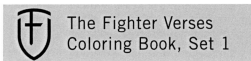
"Know therefore that the LORD your God is God, the faithful God who keeps covenant and steadfast love with those who love him and keep his commandments, to a thousand generations,"—*Deuteronomy 7:9*

God keeps His promise forever.

"And now, Israel, what does the LORD your God require of you, but to fear the LORD your God, to walk in all his ways, to love him, to serve the LORD your God with all your heart and with all your soul, [13]and to keep the commandments and statutes of the LORD, which I am commanding you today for your good?"—*Deuteronomy 10:12-13*

Do you love and obey God?

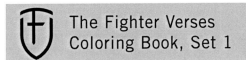
But to all who did receive him, who believed in his name, he gave the right to become children of God, [13]who were born, not of blood nor of the will of the flesh nor of the will of man, but of God.—*John 1:12-13*

Being a child of God is a gift from God.

Oh, the depth of the riches and wisdom and knowledge of God!
How unsearchable are his judgments and how inscrutable his ways!
[34]"For who has known the mind of the Lord, or who has been his
counselor?" [35]"Or who has given a gift to him that he might be repaid?"
[36]For from him and through him and to him are all things.
To him be glory forever. Amen.—*Romans 11:33-36*

Thank you, God, for saving sinful people.

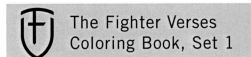
I appeal to you therefore, brothers, by the mercies of God, to present your bodies as a living sacrifice, holy and acceptable to God, which is your spiritual worship. ²Do not be conformed to this world, but be transformed by the renewal of your mind, that by testing you may discern what is the will of God, what is good and acceptable and perfect.—*Romans 12:1-2*

Dear God, help me to follow Jesus,
even when others are not.

When I am afraid, I put my trust in you. ⁴In God, whose word I praise, in God I trust; I shall not be afraid. What can flesh do to me?—*Psalm 56:3-4*

Dear Jesus, I trust you. Help me when I am afraid.

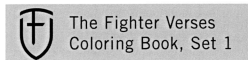

For God alone, O my soul, wait in silence, for my hope is from him.
⁶He only is my rock and my salvation, my fortress; I shall not be shaken.
⁷On God rests my salvation and my glory; my mighty rock,
my refuge is God. [⁸Trust in him at all times, O people;
pour out your heart before him; God is a refuge for us.]—*Psalm 62:5-7 [8]*

God, help me to trust you as my rock and my fortress.

There is therefore now no condemnation
for those who are in Christ Jesus.—*Romans 8:1*

Jesus died so my sins could be forgiven.

The Fighter Verses Coloring Book, Set 1 © 2015 Next Generation Resources, Inc. and Linda McIntire. Illustrations Truth78.

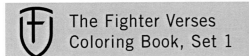
Do not love the world or the things in the world.
If anyone loves the world, the love of the Father is not in him.
¹⁶For all that is in the world—the desires of the flesh and the desires of
the eyes and pride in possessions—is not from the Father but is from the
world. ¹⁷And the world is passing away along with its desires,
but whoever does the will of God abides forever.—*1 John 2:15-17*

Love for the world doesn't last;
love for God is forever.

Have this mind among yourselves, which is yours in Christ Jesus, ⁶who, though he was in the form of God, did not count equality with God a thing to be grasped, ⁷but emptied himself, by taking the form of a servant, being born in the likeness of men.—*Philippians 2:5-7*

Be humble like Jesus.

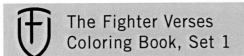
And being found in human form, he humbled himself
by becoming obedient to the point of death, even death on a cross.
⁹Therefore God has highly exalted him and bestowed on him
the name that is above every name,—*Philippians 2:8-9*

Jesus died, rose from the dead, and now reigns as King.

so that at the name of Jesus every knee should bow, in heaven and on earth and under the earth, [11]and every tongue confess that Jesus Christ is Lord, to the glory of God the Father.—*Philippians 2:10-11*

Every person will bow before King Jesus.

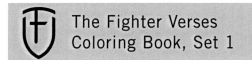

Therefore, my beloved, as you have always obeyed, so now, not only as in my presence but much more in my absence, work out your own salvation with fear and trembling, [13]for it is God who works in you, both to will and to work for his good pleasure.—*Philippians 2:12-13*

God gives His children the heart to obey Him.

Count it all joy, my brothers, when you meet trials of various kinds,
³for you know that the testing of your faith produces steadfastness.
—James 1:2-3

Trials make Christians strong.

And let steadfastness have its full effect,
that you may be perfect and complete, lacking in nothing.
⁵If any of you lacks wisdom, let him ask God, who gives generously
to all without reproach, and it will be given him.—*James 1:4-5*

God gives wisdom to His children.

Blessed is the man who walks not in the counsel of the wicked,
nor stands in the way of sinners, nor sits in the seat of scoffers;
²but his delight is in the law of the LORD,
and on his law he meditates day and night.—*Psalm 1:1-2*

A person who hates what is wrong and loves the Bible
is a happy person.

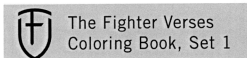

He is like a tree planted by streams of water
that yields its fruit in its season, and its leaf does not wither.
In all that he does, he prospers. ⁴The wicked are not so,
but are like chaff that the wind drives away.—*Psalm 1:3-4*

In the end, things go well for godly people,
but things go badly for the wicked.

Therefore the wicked will not stand in the judgment, nor sinners in the congregation of the righteous; ⁶for the LORD knows the way of the righteous, but the way of the wicked will perish.—*Psalm 1:5-6*

God will bring the godly to heaven but not the wicked.

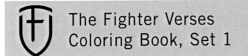
If then you have been raised with Christ, seek the things that are above, where Christ is, seated at the right hand of God. ²Set your minds on things that are above, not on things that are on earth. ³For you have died, and your life is hidden with Christ in God.—*Colossians 3:1-3*

If you love Jesus, you will think about Him.

Be angry and do not sin; do not let the sun go down on your anger,
—*Ephesians 4:26*

Be angry at sin, but do not sin when you are angry.

The Fighter Verses Coloring Book, Set 1 © 2015 Next Generation Resources, Inc. and Linda McIntire. Illustrations Truth78.

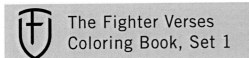
Have you not known? Have you not heard? The LORD is the everlasting God, the Creator of the ends of the earth. He does not faint or grow weary; his understanding is unsearchable. 29He gives power to the faint, and to him who has no might he increases strength.—*Isaiah 40:28-29*

God never gets tired, and He gives strength to His children.

Even youths shall faint and be weary, and young men shall fall exhausted;
[31]but they who wait for the LORD shall renew their strength;
they shall mount up with wings like eagles; they shall run
and not be weary; they shall walk and not faint.—*Isaiah 40:30-31*

If you trust in God,
He will help you do what He wants you to do.

The Fighter Verses Coloring Book, Set 1 © 2015 Next Generation Resources, Inc. and Linda McIntire. Illustrations Truth78.

For you, O Lord, are good and forgiving, abounding in steadfast love to all who call upon you. ⁶Give ear, O LORD, to my prayer; listen to my plea for grace. ⁷In the day of my trouble I call upon you, for you answer me.—*Psalm 86:5-7*

God is good and answers the prayers of His children.

The Fighter Verses Coloring Book, Set 1 © 2015 Next Generation Resources, Inc. and Linda McIntire. Illustrations Truth78.

For there is one God, and there is one mediator between God and men,
the man Christ Jesus,—*1 Timothy 2:5*

Because of Jesus' death,
I can become a friend of God.

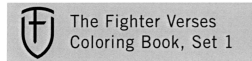
Blessed be the God and Father of our Lord Jesus Christ! According to his great mercy, he has caused us to be born again to a living hope through the resurrection of Jesus Christ from the dead, ⁴to an inheritance that is imperishable, undefiled, and unfading, kept in heaven for you, ⁵who by God's power are being guarded through faith for a salvation ready to be revealed in the last time.—*1 Peter 1:3-5*

Heaven is promised to those who are trusting in Jesus.

Finally, be strong in the Lord and in the strength of his might.
¹¹Put on the whole armor of God, that you may be able to stand
against the schemes of the devil.—*Ephesians 6:10-11*

God has given His children spiritual weapons.

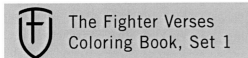
For we do not wrestle against flesh and blood, but against the rulers, against the authorities, against the cosmic powers over this present darkness, against the spiritual forces of evil in the heavenly places. ¹³Therefore take up the whole armor of God, that you may be able to withstand in the evil day, and having done all, to stand firm.
—*Ephesians 6:12-13*

God will help you to be strong in faith and to say "no" to wrong thoughts and actions.

Stand therefore, having fastened on the belt of truth, and having put on the breastplate of righteousness, [15]and, as shoes for your feet, having put on the readiness given by the gospel of peace.—*Ephesians 6:14-15*

Stand firm trusting in Jesus' death to take away your sin.

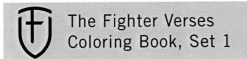

In all circumstances take up the shield of faith, with which you can extinguish all the flaming darts of the evil one; [17]and take the helmet of salvation, and the sword of the Spirit, which is the word of God, [[18]praying at all times in the Spirit, with all prayer and supplication. To that end keep alert with all perseverance, making supplication for all the saints,]—*Ephesians 6:16-17 [18]*

Fight Satan's attacks with faith and the Word of God.

And I am sure of this, that he who began a good work in you will bring it to completion at the day of Jesus Christ.—*Philippians 1:6*

God will keep His children believing in Him.

And do not fear those who kill the body but cannot kill the soul. Rather fear him who can destroy both soul and body in hell.—*Matthew 10:28*

Do not be afraid of what others might do to you; instead trust and obey God.

For I am not ashamed of the gospel, for it is the power of God for salvation
to everyone who believes, to the Jew first and also to the Greek.
[¹⁷For in it the righteousness of God is revealed from faith for faith,
as it is written, "The righteous shall live by faith."]—*Romans 1:16 [17]*

God's children are happy to tell others that
Jesus saves us from our sin.

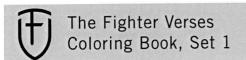

"Come to me, all you who labor and are heavy laden,
and I will give you rest. ²⁹Take my yoke upon you and learn from me,
for I am gentle and lowly in heart, and you will find rest for your souls.
³⁰For my yoke is easy and my burden is light."—*Matthew 11:28-30*

Come to Jesus and learn from Him.

Now I know that the LORD saves his anointed; he will answer him
from his holy heaven with the saving might of his right hand.
⁷Some trust in chariots and some in horses,
but we trust in the name of the LORD our God.
[⁸They collapse and fall, but we rise and stand upright.]—*Psalm 20:6-7 [8]*

We will pray and trust in God.

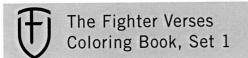
Blessed is the man who remains steadfast under trial,
for when he has stood the test he will receive the crown of life,
which God has promised to those who love him.—*James 1:12*

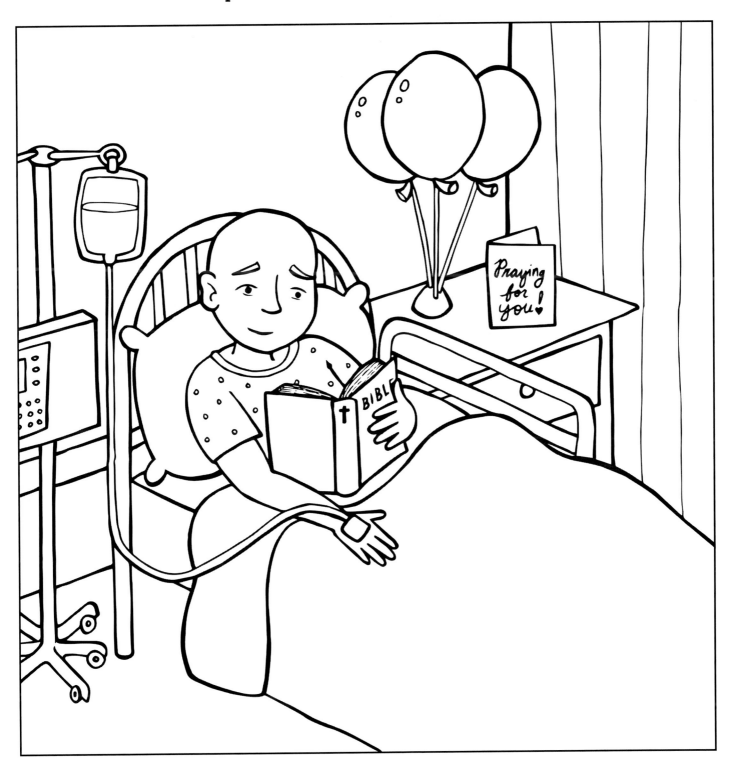

I will trust in God even when things are hard.

The point is this: whoever sows sparingly will also reap sparingly, and whoever sows bountifully will also reap bountifully. [7]Each one must give as he has decided in his heart, not reluctantly or under compulsion, for God loves a cheerful giver.—*2 Corinthians 9:6-7*

God loves cheerful giving.

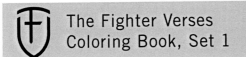
And God is able to make all grace abound to you,
so that having all sufficiency in all things at all times,
you may abound in every good work.—*2 Corinthians 9:8*

God gives His children what they need to do good to others.

But he said to me, "My grace is sufficient for you, for my power
is made perfect in weakness." Therefore I will boast all the more gladly
of my weaknesses, so that the power of Christ may rest upon me.
[¹⁰For the sake of Christ, then, I am content with weaknesses,
insults, hardships, persecutions, and calamities.
For when I am weak, then I am strong.]—*2 Corinthians 12:9 [10]*

God gives His strength to His children when things are hard for them.

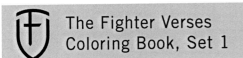
From of old no one has heard or perceived by the ear, no eye has seen a God besides you, who acts for those who wait for him. —*Isaiah 64:4*

No one has ever seen another god who does the mighty acts our God does.

But when the goodness and loving kindness of God our Savior appeared,
⁵he saved us, not because of works done by us in righteousness,
but according to his own mercy, by the washing of regeneration
and renewal of the Holy Spirit, ⁶whom he poured out on us richly
through Jesus Christ our Savior,—*Titus 3:4-6*

We cannot save ourselves. Jesus saves sinners.

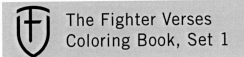
"...remember the former things of old; for I am God, and there is no other; I am God, and there is none like me, [10]declaring the end from the beginning and from ancient times things not yet done, saying, 'My counsel shall stand, and I will accomplish all my purpose,' [[11]calling a bird of prey from the east, the man of my counsel from a far country. I have spoken, and I will bring it to pass; I have purposed, and I will do it."]—*Isaiah 46:9-10 [11]*

He does what He says He will do.
He does what He plans; His plans always work out.

My son, if sinners entice you, do not consent.—*Proverbs 1:10*

Do not follow when others want you to do bad things.

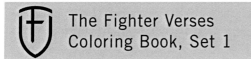
Trust in the LORD with all your heart, and do not lean on your own understanding. [6]In all your ways acknowledge him, and he will make straight your paths. [[7]Be not wise in your own eyes; fear the LORD, and turn away from evil.]—*Proverbs 3:5-6 [7]*

Trust God and ask Him for help.

Good sense makes one slow to anger,
and it is his glory to overlook an offense.—*Proverbs 19:11*

It is wise to not get angry and to forgive others.

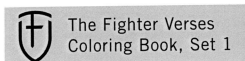
I am the vine; you are the branches.
Whoever abides in me and I in him, he it is that bears much fruit,
for apart from me you can do nothing.—*John 15:5*

Trust Jesus to be your friend and helper every day.

In my Father's house are many rooms. If it were not so,
would I have told you that I go to prepare a place for you?
³And if I go and prepare a place for you, I will come again and will take
you to myself, that where I am you may be also.—*John 14:2-3*

Jesus will return to bring Christians to heaven.
Christians will be with Jesus forever.

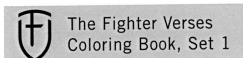
Those who trust in the LORD are like Mount Zion,
which cannot be moved, but abides forever.
²As the mountains surround Jerusalem, so the LORD surrounds his
people, from this time forth and forevermore.—*Psalm 125:1-2*

If you trust God, you will stand strong. God always
helps His people.

Set a guard, O LORD, over my mouth; keep watch over the door
of my lips! ⁴Do not let my heart incline to any evil...—*Psalm 141:3-4*

Dear Jesus, please give me a kind heart and kind words.

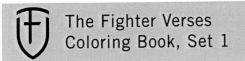
If we say we have no sin, we deceive ourselves, and the truth is not in us.
⁹If we confess our sins, he is faithful and just to forgive us our sins
and to cleanse us from all unrighteousness.—*1 John 1:8-9*

Dear Jesus, please forgive me...

The LORD is my shepherd; I shall not want. [2]He makes me lie down in green pastures. He leads me beside still waters.—*Psalm 23:1-2*

Jesus cares for His people.

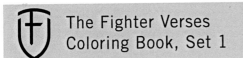
He restores my soul. He leads me in paths of righteousness
for his name's sake. ⁴Even though I walk through the valley
of the shadow of death, I will fear no evil, for you are with me;
your rod and your staff, they comfort me.—*Psalm 23:3-4*

Jesus shows His people what is right, and they are not afraid.

You prepare a table before me in the presence of my enemies;
you anoint my head with oil; my cup overflows.
⁶Surely goodness and mercy shall follow me all the days of my life,
and I shall dwell in the house of the LORD forever.—*Psalm 23:5-6*

God's goodness and kindness
to His children never end.

Bible Memory Tips

Children memorize easily. In fact, they often memorize effortlessly. Since memorization is so easy for them, they are memorizing constantly. They will memorize either what the world has to offer them or what we have to offer them. Why not take advantage of this God-given gift for the benefit of our children's spiritual growth? For many adults, the verses they know well (those which come to mind as an automatic response) are verses learned in childhood. So seize the moment!

Memory Tips for Young Children

Memorizing by repetition works well when teaching verses to young children:

- **Say the reference.** First, clearly pronounce the reference ("address" is easier for some young children to understand than "reference"). Then have the child repeat the reference.

- **Repeat the passage in sections.** Say the passage in several bite-sized sections, repeating each section. Repeat the sections.

- **Repeat the reference again.**

- **Review the passage several more times,** lengthening the sections each time.

- **Discuss the passage.** After the passage is remembered (usually in 3-4 repetitions), it is good to dissect it. Discuss the meaning of unfamiliar words. Rephrase the passage and try to help the child discover how the passage applies to his life.

Memory Tips for Older Children

- **Read the passage.**
- **Understand the passage.**
  - Look up the passage in its biblical context.
  - Have the child say or write the passage in his own words.
  - Have the child say what he thinks is the most important word and why he thinks so. Then you do the same.
  - Have the child read the passage silently and then explain what it means.
  - Have the child explain what he thinks a Christian should think, feel, and do in response to the verses. Discuss how this applies to him personally.
  - Illustrate the verse by drawing a picture.
  - Have the child act out the passage, or a situation in which it would apply.
- **Learn the passage.** Knowing what the verse means and how to apply it prepares the child to memorize it. There are several ways to memorize a section of Scripture:
  - Read the verse through completely several times.
  - Write the verse in a notebook.
  - Repeat the verse a section at a time. Repeat a section several times. Add another section until the whole verse can be said. Always review before going to bed.
- **Implement the passage.** Once the child knows what the passage means, he needs to learn to put it into practice.

We cannot always be with our children. If the word of God dwells richly in them, they have wise counsel with them at all times. In addition, God's Word is so much more powerful than our Words; it will equip them to fight the fight of faith and protect them from the attack of the enemy.

Fighter Verses is a five-year Bible memory program that encourages believers to persevere in the fight of faith by arming them with God's Word. Through Scripture memory, this powerful sword is always available to provide counsel, encouragement, and protection from the enemy of our souls. The 260 passages in the collection focus on the character and worth of God, battling fleshly desires, and the hope of the Gospel: reconciliation with God by the death of His Son.

Resources to encourage you in memorization include:

THE FIGHTER VERSES STUDY

Building relationships that are deep, lasting, and meaningful requires time spent listening and talking together. Nurturing a relationship with God is no different. The Fighter Verses Study will help you spend quality "bites" of time with God as you study the verses found in Fighter Verses, Set 1. Resources include:

- The **Discussion Guide** (with leader prompts and answer key for fathers, small group leaders, or individuals) or **Study Guide** (for study participants) will help you ponder and understand each week's Scripture passage through guided questions, which can be answered personally or discussed as a group.

- Use the **Journal** in your quiet time with the Lord to reflect on the verses and record action steps you want to take.

- The **Coloring Book** helps younger children engage during the discussion and gives them a visual representation of the main truth they will learn each week.

THE FIGHTER VERSES APP

The app contains Fighter Verses, Extended Memory Verses, Foundation Verses, and Truth78 Curriculum Verses in an easy-to-use format. Memorization is encouraged using built-in quizzes, songs, links to devotionals and commentaries, review functions, and more. Download at: iTunes, Google Play, or Amazon.

FIGHTERVERSES.COM

Read our weekly devotional blog and find resources on how to memorize Scripture, encourage children, and start a church-wide Fighter Verses program.

FIGHTER VERSES SONGS

Memorization is easier with Fighter Verses set to music. Songs mirror verses word-for-word and are set to simple tunes families love. Songs are available on FighterVerses.com, on a CD from childrendesiringGod.org, or as a download from iTunes.

FOUNDATION VERSES

Teach your 2- to 5-year-old children 76 strategically chosen Bible verses to lay a firm scriptural foundation of basic biblical truth.

FighterVerses.com